WRITING to **14**

Writing frames

Geoff Barton

OXFORD

OXFORD

UNIVERSITY PRESS

Great Clarendon Street, Oxford OX2 6DP

Oxford University Press is a department of the University of Oxford.
It furthers the University's objective of excellence in research, scholarship,
and education by publishing worldwide in

Oxford New York

Athens Auckland Bangkok Bogotá Buenos Aires Calcutta Cape Town
Chennai Dar es Salaam Delhi Florence Hong Kong Istanbul Karachi
Kuala Lumpur Madrid Melbourne Mexico City Mumbai Nairobi
Paris São Paulo Singapore Taipei Tokyo Toronto Warsaw

with associated companies in Berlin Ibadan

Oxford is a registered trade mark of Oxford University Press
in the UK and in certain other countries

First published 2000
Reprinted 2000

ISBN 0 19 831463 9

Printed in Great Britain

WRITING TO 14
Writing Frames

Introduction

This collection of photocopiable writing frames is designed to help students achieve success with *Writing to 14*. We know from the National Literacy Strategy and other projects how powerful writing frames can be for developing students' skills in thinking, planning, and writing.

The frames in this pack provide a number of elements to support students. They include:

- appropriate layouts/formats for different styles and genres
- structures to help them organize their writing
- planning sheets for brainstorming
- interview sheets for collecting data
- skills sheets to reinforce some of the essential ideas from *Writing to 14*
- sentence starters to get their writing kick-started.

The frames might prove especially helpful for less confident writers, though they are designed to support students of all abilities.

I hope that they will make your job in the classroom easier, and lead to growing confidence in writing among your students.

Geoff Barton

Contents

Thinking about audience and register

Brainstorming sheet

Assignment	Who is my **audience**? Think about their age, their background, how much they will know already about the topic, and what they will be expecting from the text.	What sort of **content** will they be interested in?	What **style** of writing will appeal to them? (Simple or complex? Serious or light-hearted? With specialist words, informal terms, slang?)
Write a leaflet for senior citizens inviting them to a Christmas concert at your school			
Write a letter to a school friend in hospital giving all the gossip from school			
Write a horror story in the style of *Point Horror* novels			
Write a letter to your Headteacher complaining about school meals			
Write an email to a friend saying how awful school meals are			
Write an article to persuade people in your class to stop eating meat			

Formal language (and when to use it)

Activity sheet: looking at synonyms

Here is a page of words and phrases. Look closely and you will find:

- six words meaning 'generous'
- six words meaning 'crash'
- six words meaning 'book'
- six words meaning 'disappear'
- six words meaning 'crowd'.

Draw lines between words which have similar meanings. (The first set of six has been done for you.) This will give you a string of words in the same area of meaning.

Then, for each string of words or phrases, use a colour code to show:

A the most formal word in each string
B the most informal word in each string

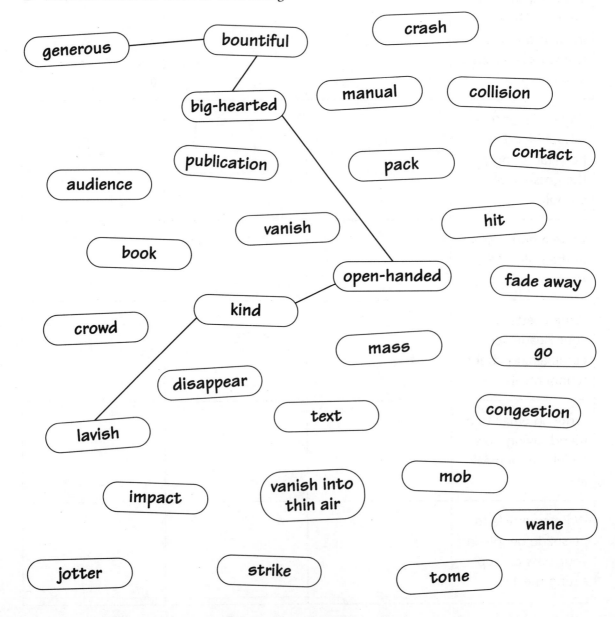

Informal language (and when to use it)

This is an imaginary letter from a Headteacher to parents, telling them about plans for a new uniform. The style is too informal. Rewrite it so that the style is appropriately formal for its audience.

**Hill Top
High School**

Dear parents

Hi! Greetings from Hill Top High! Hope you're all hanging loose and chilling out.

We've got some pretty exciting plans afoot. The real biggy is that we want to change the uniform. Blazers are a no-no. It's time to scrap them.

So instead we're introducing polo shirts, casual but smart trousers for girls and boys, and a new school sweatshirt.

We think it'll make the kids more relaxed and we won't have to hassle them about the way they're dressed any more.

But what do you think?

All comments gratefully received.

Ciao for now,

Keith Foley
Head.

Planning an essay

General essay planning frame: any 'for/against' title

TITLE:

Brainstorm ideas here, for and against.

Ideas FOR:

Specific examples:

Ideas AGAINST:

Specific examples:

Conclusion:

Essay planning frame 1

TITLE: What are the reasons for and against giving up meat?

Brainstorm ideas here, for and against.

Ideas FOR giving up meat:

Specific examples:

Ideas AGAINST giving up meat:

Specific examples:

Conclusion:

Essay planning frame 2

TITLE: Many people say that more choice of television channels has led to lower standards of programmes. What is your opinion?

Brainstorm ideas here, for and against.

Ideas FOR lower standards of programmes:	Ideas AGAINST lower standards of programmes:
Specific examples:	Specific examples:

Conclusion:

Planning an essay

TITLE: Thirty years ago, the first human being set foot on the moon. What are the arguments for and against continuing our exploration of space?

Brainstorm ideas here, for and against.

Ideas FOR continuing exploration:	Specific examples:	Ideas AGAINST continuing exploration:	Specific examples:

Conclusion:

Writing openings for literature essays

Activity sheet: sample essay openings

Here are three opening paragraphs from literature essays, written in response to this title:

> Choose a poem you enjoyed reading and write an introduction to it for a new reader.
>
> Comment on what it is about and the way it has been written.

Look at the opening paragraphs and decide:

● what are the strengths and weaknesses of each one (– think about the style, the sentences, the vocabulary, how personal they are, how much they make you want to read on…)
● which is best overall (– to help you decide, look at the title of the essay again)
● which is the weakest.

A

This is a really good poem. It's by Seamus Heaney who's an Irish poet who recently won the Whitbread Prize for poetry so he must be good. The poem is called 'Blackberry Picking' and it's all about a boy who goes off into the countryside to pick blackberries. At first it's great fun. Later he doesn't seem so happy…

B

Seamus Heaney's poem 'Blackberry Picking' looks back to his own childhood. He describes a memory of going blackberry picking and, in the first half of the poem, he writes with a real sense of pleasure and adventure. He recalls the blackberries looking 'like a plate of eyes' which reminds us of the way children see things – quite unusually and excitingly. In a similar way, he describes his hands as 'sticky as Bluebeard's', a reference to the famous pirate…

C

I chose this poem because of its really brilliant language. It describes a poet's memories of childhood and really focuses on the senses to bring the memories alive for the reader. First of all there's plenty of mention of colour – 'green', 'red', a 'glossy purple clot' and, later on, a 'rat-grey fungus'. This all really helps us to see the scene. The bright colours at the start disappear later in the poem. The rat-grey colour shows how things are spoilt and become disappointing and unpleasant…

Using quotations in literature essays

Here is the opening paragraph from a literature assignment. The author
is writing about Duke Orsino, from Shakespeare's play *Twelfth Night*,
and in particularly has been looking at the Duke's opening speech:

> If music be the food of love, play on;
> Give me excess of it, that, surfeiting,
> The appetite may sicken and so die.
> That strain again! It had a dying fall…

To practise building quotations into your sentences, choose appropriate
quotations from the speech to fill the spaces in this opening paragraph:

The opening scene shows us that the Duke is deeply in love. He compares the feeling of

love to music and says _____

_____.

Keeping the musical theme going the Duke uses words like _____

and _____. To him, love seems like something you consume.

For example, he uses the word _____

to suggest food. It is interesting that he also uses words related to death, such as

_____.

Writing a review

Book review planning frame

Factual details

Author: _____

Title: _____

Factual summary (Give three sentences saying what the story is about and who the characters are. Don't give away the ending.)

_____

_____

_____

The book's strengths

● Which characters did you especially like? Why?

_____

● Which parts of the storyline really worked well? Why?

_____

_____

● What did you enjoy about the writer's style?

_____

The book's weaknesses

● Which characters were less believable or interesting?

_____

● Which parts of the story were hard to follow / unbelievable?

_____

_____

● When did the writer's style not work so well?

_____

Summary (Your opinion of the book overall)

_____

_____

_____

Star rating

Circle the number of stars you would give this book.

   *   **   ***   ****   *****

Writing a review

Film review planning frame

Factual details

Name of film: _____

Year it was made: _____

Factual summary (Who is in it? Who directed it? What genre [category] of film is it in, e.g. adventure, comedy, animation, historical drama…?)

_____

_____

_____

Storyline (Write down three sentences about the storyline, without giving away any secrets.)

_____

_____

_____

Performances (What you liked/disliked about the way the actors played their roles)

_____

_____

The film's strengths (What you enjoyed about it – you might include technical features like camera angles, locations, musical score)

_____

_____

The film's weaknesses (How the film might have been improved)

_____

_____

Summary (Your view of the film overall)

_____

_____

_____

Star rating

Circle the number of stars you would give this film.

   *   **   ***   ****   *****

Writing a review

CD review planning frame

Factual details

Who the CD is by: _____

Title: _____

 Label (e.g. EMI, Virgin): _____

Factual summary (How many tracks, who wrote most of them, how many previous CDs this group/singer has made, the style of the music.)

_____

_____

_____

Review (Choose two or three tracks and write about them – the lyrics, the melody, the overall sound. Say what you think works well and what is less successful.)

_____

_____

_____

_____

_____

(Say which track you like best and why.)

_____

_____

_____

Overall opinion (What you think about the album overall, whether it shows the singer/group moving in a new direction/getting better/sounding the same, whether you would recommend it)

_____

_____

_____

_____

Star rating
Circle the number of stars you would give this CD.

    *   **   ***   ****   *****

Writing a biography

Research frame

Use this frame to find out about your subject's background, ready to write a short biographical feature.

Factual details

Name: _____

Date of birth: _____

Birthplace: _____

Details of early life

Who looked after you when you were little?

_____

_____

How many brothers and sisters do you have?

_____

_____

How old were they when you were born?

_____

_____

What was your first memory?

_____

_____

_____

What do you remember about nursery school?

_____

_____

_____

What do you remember about infant school?

_____

_____

_____

Writing a biography

Biography interview sheet

Use this sheet to record details of a particular incident in your subject's early life.

Name of subject: _____

Ask your subject to choose one key memory from his/her past. It can be either a positive or negative moment. Then ask the following questions and note down their answers.

When did the event happen?

_____

How old were you?

_____

Where did it happen?

_____

What exactly happened?

_____

_____

_____

_____

Can you describe the details of the scene – what it looked like, any smells/sounds/colours you remember?

_____

_____

_____

Can you remember any dialogue (conversation) from the time this happened?

_____

_____

_____

Why do you think this memory sticks in your mind so much?

_____

_____

_____

How have you changed since then?

_____

Writing a tabloid newspaper article

Tabloid writing frame

Notes
- 14-year-old Stephen Fawcett of Wrexham, North Wales is well known at school for his animal impressions
- Hears smashing of glass at local library, phones police from call box, and then waits near library
- Thinks he sees thieves coming out from the broken window
- Does an impression of an Alsatian dog – the thieves go back in
- Police arrive and arrest them

Headline ideas: _____

Paragraph one – topic sentence (summarize the whole story):

Paragraph two (say more about Stephen):

Paragraph three (say more about where this took place and what happened):

Paragraph four (give a quotation from Stephen):

Paragraph five (give some quotations from other people. For example: 'Stephen's parents X & Y said later, …'):

Paragraph six (give a quotation from the police):

Writing a broadsheet newspaper article

Broadsheet writing frame

Notes

- Professor Jane Morris, Batley University, Yorkshire says schools are letting down pupils.
- They should teach more basics and cut out anything else for first six years – i.e. no PE, no Geography, History or RE, just English, Maths and Science.
- She says: 'This would provide a far better foundation for success than the current mixed diet of learning.'

- Government spokesperson says: 'The curriculum is always under review, but we would be unwilling to create anything quite as narrow as this.'
- Educationist Don Bousted says: 'I am appalled that anyone would suggest this. School should be about more than just learning basics. It is where children learn a whole range of skills. To scrap these would be a disaster.'

Headline ideas: _____

Paragraph 1 (summarize the whole story):

Paragraph 2 (say something about Professor Jane Morris):

Paragraph 3 (quote something by her):

Paragraph 4 (give the Government response):

Paragraph 5 (quote educationist Don Bousted):

Writing frame

Use this frame to complete the 'Star Wars' story:

Star Wars sets UK record

The Phantom Menace: Breaking box office records in the UK

Star Wars: Episode 1 – The Phantom Menace has broken UK box office records, raking in $15.1m (£9.5m) in its first four days.

The previous record holder in Britain was Independence Day, another sci-fi blockbuster, which took £6.9m ($10.8m) in July 1996 over its first weekend.

The Phantom Menace opened in the UK on 15 July. And despite the weekend of glorious weather that followed, thousands of eager fans found the lure of George Lucas's long-awaited Star Wars prequel too great to stay outdoors.

There were huge queues outside cinemas on the opening Thursday and they continued throughout the weekend.

A spokesperson for Warner Cinemas, Julie Thomas, said _____

_____

_____

_____

She added that yesterday alone _____

_____

_____

Meanwhile the fans of the film seemed positive. Saskia Macey, 12, from

Stowmarket, said: _____

_____

_____

_____

But film critic Leonard Vaux pointed out that _____

_____

_____

He added: _____

_____

_____

Using wordplay in headlines and slogans

Headline / slogan planning sheet

Remember the different techniques:

- Alliteration is the repetition of the sounds at the start of words ('Pick up a Penguin')
- Puns are jokes which use unexpected words – 'Kentucky Freed Chicken'
- Full rhyme: 'St Helen's Glass has the Class' (full rhyme of 'glass' and 'class')
- Half-rhyme: 'Beenz Meanz Heinz' (half-rhyme of 'Meanz' and 'Heinz')

Try out your ideas in these boxes:

Headlines	Slogans
High exam results at your school	New low-sugar high-caffeine soft drink
A huge storm over your town	New watch, in which you can change the colour of its display
A footballer's shorts fall down during an important game	Supermarket claims lowest prices and fastest queues

Writing a feature article

General planning frame

Topic: _____

Who is my audience?

_____

_____

What will they be interested in?

_____

_____

What do they already know about the subject?

_____

_____

Notes on the style I will use:

_____

_____

What I already know about the subject:

_____

_____

What I need to find out:

_____

_____

Facts researched (in note form):

_____

_____

_____

Notes on the vocabulary I will want to use:

_____

_____

Writing a feature article

Topic: _____

Factual details about the event

What it was: _____

_____

When it happened: _____

Where it happened: _____

Who was involved: _____

_____

Comments on the event from people involved:

Name: _____

Comment: _____

_____

Name: _____

Comment: _____

_____

Name: _____

Comment: _____

_____

Comments from people who were spectators/audience:

Name: _____

Comment: _____

_____

Name: _____

Comment: _____

_____

Name: _____

Comment: _____

_____

Writing a feature article

Planning sheet for article on a hobby or activity

Topic: _____

Factual details about the hobby/activity

Name of hobby/activity: _____

What it involves: _____

Who does it: _____

Age-range it most appeals to: _____

_____

Interview with someone who does this activity

Name: _____

Age: _____

1 Why are you interested in it?

_____

_____

_____

2 What skills does it involve?

_____

_____

3 When did you start?

_____

4 Would you recommend it to other people?

_____

5 Why / why not?

_____

_____

_____

_____

_____

Writing a feature article

Planning sheet for a personal profile article

Name of person to be profiled: _____

Factual details

Age: _____

Background: _____

Job: _____

How long s/he has been doing this job: _____

Interview questions

1 Why did you come into this job? _____

_____

2 What did you do before? _____

_____

3 What do you like about the job? _____

_____

4 What did you do before? _____

_____

_____

5 What skills do you need for this job? _____

_____

_____

6 What is the main reward from this job? _____

_____

_____

7 What is the main frustration? _____

_____

_____

8 What do you think you will be doing in the future? _____

_____

_____

Writing a report 1 – factual reports

Factual report frame

Keep your language clear and straightforward. Don't let sentences get too long.

Aim
(What I am trying to achieve)

Method
(How I approached the task)

Step 1

Step 2

Step 3

Step 4

Results
(Table:)

(What the table shows)

Conclusion
(What I found out)

(Were the results expected or unexpected?)

I might have approached the task differently by...

Writing a report 1 – factual reports

Police report frame

Information

- 7.45 yesterday morning – you were doing paper-round
- heard crash of glass at 34 Manor Garth
- then nothing – then man in blue T-shirt running with video
- dark hair – in his twenties – jeans – white trainers
- ran down drive, along passage to playing field
- you ran to 37, knocked on door and asked them to phone police

Describe what happened in the order in which it happened.
Be as precise as possible about who, where, when, etc.

I was _____

_____

when I heard _____

_____ .

At first _____

_____ .

Then I saw _____

_____

_____

_____

_____

_____

_____

I _____

_____

_____

_____

_____

_____

Writing a report 2 – reports which entertain

Uniform survey writing frame

Imagine that you have been asked to write a report on student attitudes to school uniform. Your report will be used by your Headteacher to consider small changes to the current code of dress.
Keep your style factual and straightforward, and if you include comments from students, show their words in inverted commas (speech marks).
This writing frame will help you to structure your report.

Introduction

This report aims to show _____

_____

In order to research this area, I have _____

_____

_____

_____

Student comments

Some students have made negative/positive* remarks about school uniform, such as

_____

_____

_____

However, other students have said _____

_____

_____

_____

Results and statistics

Overall, the survey has shown that _____

_____

_____

Conclusion

I therefore recommend that _____

_____

_____

*Delete one of these

Persuasive language in advertising

Here is another boring advertisement. Make it more effective.

SCREAMERS

Screamers are the nice new sports shoe
for people who like sports.
They are really smart and trendy.

Put on a pair of Screamers
and everyone will look at you.

Screamers are built to
protect your feet too, so
they're really a very
good product.

Screamers.
Buy some please.

Rewritten advertisement:

Using emotive language

Leaflet writing frame 1: portrait format

Purpose: to persuade readers to give up eating meat
Audience: young people aged 11-16

Headline

Subheading

Text

Image – quick sketch

Subheading

Text

Slogan

Leaflet writing frame 2: landscape format

Purpose:
Audience:

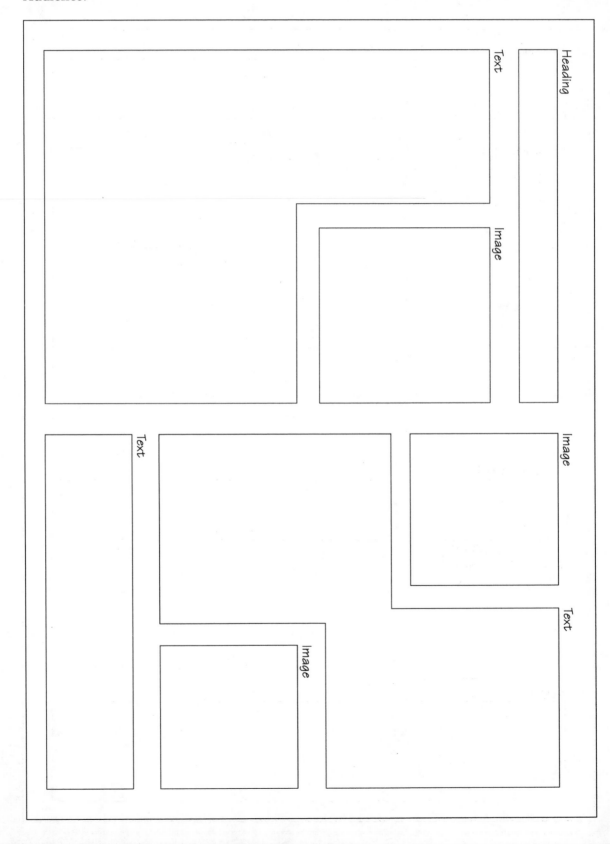

Writing a leaflet

Planning frame

Before constructing your leaflet, use this frame to plan what you will include.

Topic:

Audience:
What arguments I will use to persuade them:

Style:
(Informative, practical, factual, persuasive, informal, formal?)

Some words/phrases I will aim to include:

Some language features I will aim to include:
(Questions, bullet-points, comments/quotations, verbless sentences, slogans, puns, alliteration?)

Ideas for the image/s I will use:

Writing a brochure

Planning frame

To help you write a brochure, use this planning frame.

Audience:

Topic:

Purpose:

Some words and phrases I might use:
(e.g. 'sun-kissed beaches')

Some sentence patterns I might use:
(e.g. imperatives: 'Just relax'; declarative sentences: 'Time has passed by this place of peaceful charms')

Style:
(Informal or formal, factual, fun, friendly, impersonal?)

Practice a few sentences here:

Factsheet: schools in the future

Speech topic:
Why schools will become less important as people have more technology at home for self-guided learning.

Sources of learning
People used to rely on schools for learning. Now they can use:

- books
- libraries
- CD-Roms
- the internet

The internet has around 200 million users.

A new website is created every 10 seconds.

Computer technology
Costs halve and performance doubles every year.

The internet gives people access to all the best libraries and reference books around the world. Computers can give personal feedback on your learning – measuring test scores and highlighting strengths and weaknesses.

People need to learn how to work with each other – problem-solving and teamwork are essential skills. Computers can't teach you this.

Factsheet: young people and responsibility

Speech topic:

Why young people in the UK should be given more responsibility at an earlier age.

Children's rights were laid down in the United Nations Convention on the Rights of the Human Child. Here is a summary of key points:

Everyone has human rights, including children. Because they are young, however, children are more likely than adults to have their rights forgotten about or ignored. To protect children's rights the United Nations has drawn up an international agreement called the United Nations Convention on the Rights of the Child.

The Convention sets out a number of articles, the rights which all children and young people up to the age of 18 should have. The rights should apply to young people everywhere, whether they live in rich or poor countries. The Convention says children have three main rights which must be considered whenever any decision is being made about them, or any action is taken which affects them.

Best interests

When adults or organizations make decisions which affect children they must always think first about what would be best for the child.

The child's views

Children too have a right to say what they think about anything which affects them. What they say must be listened to carefully. When courts or other official bodies are making decisions which affect children they must listen to what the children want and feel.

Discrimination

Every child regardless of race, colour, sex, language, religion or disability should be protected from all kinds of discrimination.

Children can:

- have a part-time job from 14
- marry with parents' consent at 16
- marry without their consent at 18
- drive a car in the UK at 17
- vote at 18.

Children in the twenty-first century reach puberty earlier than they did a century ago – they grow up physically faster. Some people argue that this should lead to a change in the law.

Factsheet: school uniform

Speech topic:
Why school uniform is / is not a good idea:

Uniform: a prescribed identifying set of clothes for members of an organization
Uniformity: a state or condition in which everything is regular

Collins English Dictionary

Here are some of the opinions expressed on an American internet discussion-site:

'School uniforms would save parents money.'

'School uniforms would save parents time. Kids in the morning would not have to make up their minds on what to wear.'

'Kids whose parents would not or could not buy them the newest fad, would not be embarrassed or harassed because of their clothes.'

'Kids' social standing would be based more on individual character and less on their economic status.'

'Lots of gangs use clothes to identify themselves and other gangs.'

'School uniforms are expensive and have no use outside of school.'

'School uniforms will do nothing but cut down on a student's individuality. A uniform is not the way to cut down on school violence. The only thing that will cut down on school violence is if parents would pay attention to their children and keep their children out of trouble and give them consequences when they disobey and not to let them run wild.'

'It is my opinion that school is in the "business" of learning. School is the place where the next lawyers, bankers, CPAs and Doctors are given the fundamentals of working in this economy. One of the basics of our culture in the working world is conservative dressing, dress code, or even uniforms. What is wrong with sending our kids the message that they are in "the business of learning" by enforcing dress codes, or even ascribing a uniform?'

In the UK, school uniforms are expected in most schools, though they vary. It is up to a school's Governing Body whether a uniform is expected. Most private schools have formal uniforms.

Writing a speech

Opening
(Aim to catch the listeners' attention. Signal what the speech will be about.)

Structure
(The different points/topics you might cover, in order)

Facts / statistics to include

Conclusion
(How you might end your speech)

Planning sheet: the day I was born

To get a detailed picture of the day you were born, you should interview someone who was there. Use these prompts to guide your questions.

Interviewer: _____

Interviewee: _____

Facts

> **When I was born**
>
> What day of the week:
>
> Time:
>
> Place:
>
> Who was there:

> **Details about the birth**
>
> How long labour took:
>
> Any problems/ complications:

> **Comments of someone who was there:**
>
> What was the hospital like?
>
> What was the midwife/doctor like?
>
> What was the weather like that day?
>
> What was in the news / music charts at that time?

Writing autobiography

Planning sheet: early memories / an incident from childhood

1 Brainstorm possible events from childhood:

Age:

What happened:

Age:

What happened:

Age:

What happened:

2 Focus on one event, and build up a picture of it:

Background details

My age: Where I was:

Time: Place:

Weather:

Who was there:

Details of senses

Things I saw:

Things I heard:

Things I smelt:

Things I tasted:

Things I touched:

Opening sentence
(Make it attention-grabbing)

Now continue your sentence into a paragraph that will make the reader want to read on.

Writing a formal letter

Formal letter frame

Your address

Date

Name of person you are writing to

Job title

Address

Greeting – Mr/Mrs/Ms Last name

Dear

Topic sentence – what the letter is about

Main body of letter

Sign-off – 'Yours sincerely'/'Yours faithfully'

Your signature

Informal letter frame

Your address

Date

Greeting – first name

Dear

Opening sentence (informal style)

Main body of letter

Sign-off

Signature (first name)

Writing a summary

Use this text to produce a summary.

The first time he spoke lines to a camera, he blew them. A couple of pictures later he spoke his lines perfectly, but he was buried so deep in a dark scene that he couldn't be seen. Toward the end of his first year as an actor, he had a nice little scene with a major star on a major production, and he found a good-looking pair of glasses that he thought gave him a bit of character. But Rock Hudson thought the same thing when he saw the kid wearing them, and Clint had to surrender his specs to the leading man.

This was Clint Eastwood's life as an eager young contract player at Universal circa 1955, and it turned out to be a short one – the studio dropped him after a year and a half. On his own, he did what young actors do: played scenes in acting classes, worked out at the gym, went on auditions, did odd jobs (mostly he dug swimming pools under the hot sun of the San Fernando Valley). Every once in a while he got an acting job – on *Highway Patrol,* on *Death Valley Days.* Once a big time show flew him east to work on location on *West Point Stories.* He got to bully James Garner on an episode of *Maverick.* A couple of times his heart leapt up: he got good billing in a feature, *The First Travelling Saleslady,* playing opposite Carol Channing; and he thought for a while that he had one of the leads in another feature, *Lafayette Escadrille.* But the first film was a flop, and he had to settle for a much smaller role in the second. When he finally got a decent part in a movie, it was in a B western so bad it almost caused him to quit the business.

Writing instructions

Writing frame for instructions

Task or process:

Equipment you will need:

Step one:

↓

Step two:

↓

Step three:

↓

Step four:

↓

Step five:

↓

Handy hints:

Thinking up ideas for stories

Use this list of questions to get yourself thinking of a character, setting and story opening. Look at each question and write the first idea that comes into your mind.

Setting

- When is your story set?

- Where is it – outdoors or indoors?

- Describe one detail of the scene (e.g. building, tree, desert, empty street):

- What is the place called?

- Who lives there?

Character

- Who is your main character?

- Who does s/he live with?

- How old is s/he?

- What does s/he look like?

- What is s/he interested in?

Storyline

- What is the first thing that happens?

- Why does it happen?

- How do people react?

Planning a storyline

Writing frame

Name of fairytale:

Summary of the story in three to five steps

1

2

3

4

5

Telling the story from the beginning

Telling the story from step 2 or 3

Knowing your audience

Activity sheet: Sarah's story

Take the opening of this story and rewrite it for a teenage audience.
The current version is too babyish – in language and emotional level.
Experiment with changes to content, characters, setting, vocabulary,
and sentences so that it suits the target audience better.
Edit the story here. Then write your rewritten version in the box below.

Sarah sat on the beach. She watched the waves. They were really big. It was early morning and the whole village seemed to be waking up around her. She loved being on holiday in France. The sky was bright blue and it promised to be a glorious day. At the back of the beach a dark car suddenly drove up. Three men got out. They ran into a small shop. Sarah could hear shouting. She was very worried. She wondered what to do.

Rewritten version:

Presenting characters by telling

Descriptive writing frame

Choose someone you know well – a friend, parent or close relative –
and write about her/him as a character in a story. Imagine that s/he is
being introduced at the start of a chapter.

Person's name:

Situation (e.g. at work, eating lunch…):

Appearance (clothes, height, build, body language, stance, gestures):

Mannerisms or habits:

Thoughts (about her/himself, the past, the future, other people):

Hopes (in the near future and the longer term):

Presenting characters by showing

Character grid

Extract	Character point	Main clue
The man shuffled towards the run-down house.	The man is old or infirm.	'Shuffled' suggests he cannot walk well – because he is either old or ill.
Rita sat on the bottom step and placed her head in her hands.		
He sat outside the room and again touched his collar, then his tie.		
Kay moved quickly from the armchair to her desk. There she began writing frantically.		
As he listened to the student's story, Mr Parker's hands tightened.		

Presenting characters by showing

Write five more sentences about Andy, filling in the blanks to give a
message about how Andy speaks and what sort of mood he is in.
To get you started, try to show Andy as sarcastic and then really happy.

1 Andy _____.

  'You'll be lucky,' he _____

  _____.

  Character message: Andy is sarcastic.

2 Andy _____.

  'You'll be lucky,' he _____

  _____.

  Character message: Andy is happy.

3 Andy _____.

  'You'll be lucky,' he _____

  _____.

  Character message: _____

4 Andy _____.

  'You'll be lucky,' he _____

  _____.

  Character message: _____

5 Andy _____.

  'You'll be lucky,' he _____

  _____.

  Character message: _____

Getting the amount of description right

Look more closely at the piece of descriptive writing below. If you were the writer's editor, which parts would recommend him to cut or change, and why? Use the grid below to give reasons for your cuts.

- Highlight or underline the parts of the text you suggest cutting/changing. Write in the new text.
- Label the cuts or changes A, B, C, etc.
- Use the comment box to say why you would cut the text.

Jenkins was sitting in a seat in an aircraft. He was wearing a navy blue suit, though he wished that he had taken off his jacket. He had a tie on that had the logo of his company on it. It was an unusually hot day for Heathrow in the spring. The pilot was waiting for clearance to take off. The cabin crew had sealed the doors and were walking up and down to check that everyone had fastened their seatbelts. A man near the back was sweating and closing his eyes. A child at the front was yelling. Jenkins got out his newspaper and thought what a long flight it was going to be.

	Why I would cut/change this text
A	
B	
C	
D	
E	

Using dialogue to reveal character

Exploring 'said'

When is 'said' the best word to use with dialogue and when should you use other verbs?

Use this extract to decide the right balance. Also experiment with whether to place the verb before or after the name of the speaker.

'Good morning Jennifer,' _____ Mr Jones _____.

'Morning, sir,' _____ Jennifer _____.

'Homework?' _____ Mr Jones _____.

'Sorry?' _____ Jennifer _____.

'You know – the homework you owe me – the piece about birds,' _____

Mr Jones _____.

'Oh, er, I see,' _____ Jennifer _____.

'You haven't done it, have you?' _____ Mr Jones _____.

'Well, I have, kind of,' _____ Jennifer _____.

'Kind of …?' _____ Mr Jones _____.

'I had a problem, I'm afraid,' _____ Jennifer _____.

'A problem? And what might that be?' _____ Mr Jones_____.

'Well, you know it was all about birds,'_____ Jennifer _____.

'Er, yes,' _____ Mr Jones _____.

'Well,' _____ Jennifer _____. 'I'm afraid my cat ate it.'

Possible verbs (though you don't have to try to use all of these):

agreed	enquired	repeated	shouted
announced	exclaimed	replied	stammered
asked	muttered	responded	stated
declared	reiterated	retorted	whispered
disclosed	remarked	said	

Making places seem real

Planning frame – task 1

Two people are setting up a picnic in a place you know.
The weather looks threatening.

Person 1

Name:

Age:

Appearance:

Background:

Person 2

Name:

Age:

Appearance:

Background:

Place

Sights:

Sounds:

Colours:

Textures:

Weather

Describe it:

Making places seem real

Planning frame – task 2

You walk into your own home and find that the electricity and telephone are not working.

Your home – description

Name of the room you walk into:

Sights:

Sounds:

Smells:

Colours:

Textures:

You try the light switch

Describe flicking the switch:

Your reaction:

Your feelings:

You pick up the telephone

Describe lifting receiver:

Describe sound:

Your reaction:

Your feelings:

Fitting characters into realistic settings

Planning frame

Jane's appearance:

Reason for travelling, and why she needs to be there on time:

Details about the people on the station:

Details about the waiting room – heating, colour of the walls, people in it:

Dramatic vocabulary to describe train passing through:

Station announcement in direct speech:

Reaction of the people – how they look and what they say:

Details of station buffet as Jane enters:

Building a storyline

Story planning sheet

Use this sheet to plan the main stages in your story. Jot down a brief summary of what happens in each section. Remember that you can use:

- one event following another
- cuts to other points of view/scenes
- flashbacks to earlier events.

Stage one:

↓

Stage two:

↓

Stage three:

↓

Stage four:

↓

Stage five:

Making a chronological story interesting

Story planning sheet

Story summary:

- Harry drives to the zoo.
- Parks car, buys ticket, goes in
- Watches the monkeys, goes to the lions

Tell the story for 5-8 year olds, trying to avoid using the phrase 'and then'.

Paragraph 1:

Paragraph 2:

Paragraph 3:

Paragraph 4:

Paragraph 5:

Writing non-chronological stories

Story grid

Kate is working late. She phones her partner Phil to tell him she will be delayed. They had a row this morning and she's happy not to rush home. But… it's Kate's birthday and Phil has arranged a surprise party. He has a house full of 40 guests. They're all sitting there waiting for Kate to return…

Use this structure to tell the story. Fill in what happens in each scene.

1 Kate at the office/phones Phil (from Kate's point of view)

2 Flashback to this morning (from Kate's point of view)

3 Meanwhile, Phil is planning a party (from Phil's point of view)

4 Kate sets off home – discovers party (from Kate's point of view)

Exploring viewpoint

Story grid

Choose two or three viewpoints and write the opening paragraph of the story in the Students' Book to see how well it works. Then write a comment in the box below.

Possible viewpoints:

Omniscient narrator (not showing us any single character's point of view):	Comment:
Ray or Sarah:	Comment:
The girl:	Comment:
The man in the car:	Comment:
Other bystander:	Comment:
Girl's mother:	Comment:

Writing strong story openings

Activity sheet: three bad openings

Choose one or two of these story openings and rewrite them to make them more interesting. Then in the box below, write two or three sentences explaining the changes you have made.

A	B	C
The sea was really deep and I felt a bit afraid of walking further down the beach into it.	Mrs Newgate knew that something was wrong when she heard a rather strange sound that she hadn't heard before and worried what it might be, so she decided to go downstairs and investigate.	'I cannot tolerate this any longer,' said Todd and he walked out of the room in a huff.
Rewritten version:	Rewritten version:	Rewritten version:
Commentary:	Commentary:	Commentary:

Building tension

Take the scenario below and practise creating tension in it, using

1 lots of short sentences to build tension
(e.g. Amanda walked more quickly. What was that? She thought she'd heard something. Nothing. She walked on.)
2 atmospherics – emotive words which create tension
(e.g. dark, unknown, prison, shock, cold, fear)
3 delaying action to keep the reader waiting.

Boy on holiday with parents. Swims to small island not far from the beach he's been lying on. Briefly explores island. Comes back to see the tide has moved in fast. The island is going to be submerged and the crossing back to the beach is getting wider. He has to swim for it…

Describe him coming back from exploring, seeing the change in the current, deciding what to do, and then build the tension as he begins to swim in deep water across to the beach.

Getting the tense right

Writing frame

Take the story idea below and experiment with different tenses.

Stephen moves to new school. It's his first day and he's terrified. He thinks back to this time last week when he was at his last school – how much safer and more pleasant it had seemed.

1	In the present tense

Stephen moves to Walton High. Walking up the long drive in his new uniform, he notices how big the building looks. He

2	In the past tense

Stephen changed schools to Walton High. As he walked up the long drive in his new uniform, he noticed how large the building looked. He

Choosing the right vocabulary

Editing sheet

Look at this terrible story opening. Use a red pen to edit and rewrite.
Then in the commentary box write two or three sentences explaining
why you made some of the changes.

The sun, a huge golden globe, beat down from amid an azure
sky. On the crowded beach below, a frenetic blaze of activity
was taking place with people running madly around, playing
giddy games, diving bravely into the clear blue attractive
seas of the beautiful bay. Shane sat confidently astride his
newly-purchased lilo, which bobbed gently upon the lapping
waves of the salty sea. He felt the sun's rays biting into his
pink shoulders and realized immediately that he should have
applied more lavishly a layer of suntan cream. Too late, he
thought introspectively, and pulled on the plastic goggles he
had persuaded his parents to purchase for him earlier that
day at the corner shop which was piled high with various
items for tourists and holidaymakers.

Commentary box

(Mention changes to sentence types, vocabulary, dialogue, amount of description, tone.)

Style features of different genres

Support sheet: sentence starters

Use these opening sentences to help you write in different genres.
Feel free to change or adapt them as you wish.

Character: Frank Rogers
Age: 47

Genre 1   **War story:** Frank Rogers is sheltering with his troops in a hut.

The thud of a shell landing some way off woke Frank from his dozing. He looked around the small, cramped hut....

Genre 2   **Science fiction:** Frank Rogers gets home from work. Automated systems welcome him back, prepare his meal, etc.

Frank scanned his ID across the security tablet. The main door slid sideways and he stepped into the hallway. The lights bloomed and his favourite CD started up. He was home at last...

Genre 3   **Horror:** Frank Rogers finds himself in a large crate. A hatch opens and a tarantula is pushed inside.

In the darkness Frank couldn't make out what the black shape might be. He only knew what he hoped it wouldn't be. Then the shape delicately moved to the corner of the crate...

Genre 4   **Romance:** Frank Rogers starts work at a new office and notices that the boss – Stacey Quinton – seems to be deliberately ignoring him.

He sat at his desk and wondered what he'd done wrong. Maybe if he was to email Stacey saying how much he was enjoying the new job but would like to ask her a few questions – maybe after work. He clicked on the email program and thought what he should say...

Genre 5   **Spy story:** Frank Rogers hovers at the edge of a street in a European city watching a man sipping coffee at a street café.

The street was quiet. The man had a newspaper in front of him and seemed to be considering whether to start the crossword. No, thought Frank, that could take hours, and we don't have hours. The man reached into his pocket...